Traveling QUILTER PLANNER

FIRST EDITION

RONA HERMAN

PUBLISHED BY RONA THE RIBBITER, LLC

Copyright @2021 All rights reserved.
Published by Rona the Ribbiter, LLC
6925 Medlin Road
Monroe, NC 28112

www.RonatheRibbiter.com

ISDN: 978-1-7371605-2-6
            978-1-7371605-3-3

Printed in the United States.
1st Printing.

Credits:
Designed by: Lindsie Bergevin

TABLE OF CONTENTS

1. Getting Started 1

2. Shop Hop Road Trip 11

3. Quilt Show Adventure 19

4. Quilt Retreats 27

5. Quilt Tours 35

6. Quilt Cruises 39

7. Fun on the Road 45

8. Quilt Coloring Pages 57

9. Appendix 67
   - Notes
   - Draw Your Quilty Inspiration
   - Answer Keys
   - Quilting Cheat Sheet

CHAPTER ONE

Getting Started

"JOBS FILL YOUR POCKET,
BUT ADVENTURE FILLS YOUR SOUL."

- JAMIE LYN BEATTY

HEY THERE FELLOW TRAVELING QUILTER!

Are you tired of the 'COVD Blues'? Ready to hit the road for some Quilting fun!? Are you picturing yourself gathered with your fellow quilters at a fabulous Quilt Retreat center doing nothing but sewing and enjoying each other's company? Are you planning to hit the road for an adventure filled cross country trip to visit family while stopping at every quilt shop along the way? Or, perhaps you're simply ready to visit an in-person Quilt Show again. Whichever your goal, the Traveling Quilter Planner is for you!

I'm an "old school" list person. So, when planning any of my various quilting adventures I need to have all the information written out in one place so I don't forget anything. Sadly, search as I may, I couldn't find a good planner anywhere that had everything I'd need all in one place. So, I wrote one!

Now you have all the same packing lists, planning sheets, and checklists you'll need for everything from Shop Hop road trips to Quilt Tours, Cruises and everything in between. Plus, there's even extra room to list out your quilt projects and supplies lists for every quilting adventure!

HOW TO USE THIS BOOK

Because I've added lists and worksheets for so many different adventures, to get the most out of your Traveling Quilter Planner I'd suggest copying the specific pages you need for your current adventure. That way, all the pages will be ready and waiting to use over and over for all your future travels.

Plus, if you are traveling with fellow quilters (hello road trip!) you can make several copies of the Word Games and coloring pages so that everyone can join in on the fun!

TRAVEL TRACKER

Where are my adventures taking me?

MY BUCKET LIST

Quilt Show Adventures

_____

_____

_____

_____

_____

_____

_____

Quilt Workshops I Want to Take

_____

_____

_____

_____

_____

_____

_____

MY BUCKET LIST

Quilt Tour and/or Cruise Adventures

_____

_____

_____

_____

_____

_____

_____

_____

_____

Quilt Projects I Want to Make

_____

_____

_____

_____

_____

_____

_____

_____

_____

_____

MONTHLY GOALS

JANUARY	FEBRUARY

MARCH	APRIL

MAY	JUNE

JULY

AUGUST

SEPTEMBER

OCTOBER

NOVEMBER

DECEMBER

BASIC PACKING LIST

Every travel adventure requires the basic necessities. Use this packing list as a base for all of your Quilting Travel Adventures.

- Pants
- Shorts
- T-shirts
- Sweatshirt
- Socks
- Underclothes
- Pajamas
- Tennis shoes / Hiking boots
- Flip Flops / Sandals
- Raincoat / Jacket
- Bathing Suit
- Face Masks
- Toiletries
- Hair Products
- Sunscreen
- Hat
- Sunglasses
- Medications
- Chargers for all electronics
- Emergency Contact list

- Headlamp / Mini Flashlight
- Reading Material
- Snacks
- Cell Phone / Tablet
- Headphones
- Travel Pillow
- All Tickets and Reservation information
- Passport
- Pen and Pad of Paper
- Water Bottle
- Hand Sanitizer
- Disinfecting Wipers
- Travel Hand Soap
- Travel Laundry Soap
- No Contact Door Opener
- Money Belt
- Several Ziploc bags, just in case
- Quilt or Other Sewing Project

- _____
- _____
- _____
- _____
- _____
- _____
- _____
- _____

- _____
- _____
- _____
- _____
- _____
- _____
- _____
- _____

PRE-TRIP CHECKLIST

- Fill enough prescriptions for duration of trip. A few extra if possible.
- Check the weather at your planned destination.
- Purchase Travel Insurance
- Make copies of all travel information to keep with a loved one.
- Inform the bank and credit card companies of travel dates and locations.
- Add Secured VPN to all electronic devices.
- Place a hold on your mail service.

ROAD TRAVEL

- Check all items in emergency roadside kit are current and not expired.
- Get the car serviced. Have them check your tires, all fluid levels, air filter, battery function and all lights and blinkers are in working order.

AIR TRAVEL

- TSA locks and keys are attached to your suitcase(s).
- Name and phone number card is placed inside your luggage.
- Check passport is up to date. (Especially for international travel)
- Sign up for TSA precheck and/or Global Entry. These programs help you get through TSA checkpoints faster and easier.
- Pack your medications, prescription copy, change of clothes and chargers in your carry-on bag in case your luggage gets lost.

ITEMS YOU CAN NOT TAKE ON AN AIRPLANE

The following items will need to be packed inside your checked baggage:

- All blades longer than 4 inches
- Rotary Cutter and blades
- Seam ripper
- Cutting Mat
- Iron

CHAPTER TWO

Shop Hop Road Trip

"WE TRAVEL TO SEEK OTHER STATES,
OTHER LIVES, OTHER SOULS."

– ANAIS NIN

Travel Dates:

LODGING INFORMATION

Contact Name: Phone:

Address:

Website:

Number of Nights: Cost:

Check-in Date: Check-Out Date:

Contact Name: Phone:

Address:

Website:

Number of Nights: Cost:

Check-in Date: Check-Out Date:

Contact Name: Phone:

Address:

Website:

Number of Nights: Cost:

Check-in Date: Check-Out Date:

QUILT SHOP LIST

Dates: _____ Budget: _____

Store Name: _____ Phone: _____

Address: _____

_____

Hours of Operation: _____

Website: _____

Dates: _____ Budget: _____

Store Name: _____ Phone: _____

Address: _____

_____

Hours of Operation: _____

Website: _____

Dates: _____ Budget: _____

Store Name: _____ Phone: _____

Address: _____

_____

Hours of Operation: _____

Website: _____

SHOP HOP BUDGET WORKSHEET

Travel

Total Miles /	Miles per Gallon =	Gallons
Gallons x $	per gallon = $	Total cost

Food

Number of days x $30 per day =	Food Budget

Lodging

Number of nights x $	per night =	Total

Fabric!

$ _____ per quilt shop x _____ number of shops = $

Travel _____

Food _____

Lodging _____

Fabric _____

Extra _____

TOTAL _____

DAILY SCHEDULE

Use this page to write your daily schedule plan.

Date:

Planned Item: Time:

Date:

Planned Item: Time:

PACKING LIST FOR THE CAR

Just in Case Items

- First Aid Kit
- Extra Batteries
- Extra Quilt
- Re-Usable Tote Bag(s)
- Laundry Basket
- Umbrella
- Towel / Hand Towel(s)

- _____
- _____
- _____
- _____

Lunch Stop Items

- Re-usable Dinnerware set
- Travel Mug
- Re-usable Utensils
- Paper Towels
- Ziploc Bags
- Garbage Bags
- Cleaning Basin for re-usables
- Travel dish soap

- _____
- _____
- _____

EVERYTHING ELSE

Little Purse Kit

- Band-Aids bandages
- Neosporin
- Antiseptic Wipes
- Small sewing kit
- Ibuprofen (or aspirin)

- Small notebook and pen
- Clothes-pins
- Hand sanitizer
- Touchless opener

Overnight Bag

- Change of clothes
- Medications
- Pajamas
- Bathroom supplies

- _____
- _____
- _____
- _____

FOOD PACKING LIST

Breakfast Items

- _____
- _____
- _____
- _____
- _____
- _____
- _____
- _____

- _____
- _____
- _____
- _____
- _____
- _____
- _____
- _____

Lunch Items

- _____
- _____
- _____
- _____
- _____
- _____
- _____
- _____

- _____
- _____
- _____
- _____
- _____
- _____
- _____
- _____

Snack Items

- _____
- _____
- _____
- _____
- _____
- _____
- _____
- _____
- _____

- _____
- _____
- _____
- _____
- _____
- _____
- _____
- _____
- _____

Dinner Items

- _____
- _____
- _____
- _____
- _____
- _____
- _____
- _____

- _____
- _____
- _____
- _____
- _____
- _____
- _____
- _____

CHAPTER THREE

Quilt Show Adventure

"LIVE LIFE WITH NO EXCUSES,
TRAVEL WITH NO REGRETS."

- OSCAR WILDE

QUILT SHOW DETAILS

Name: Date:

Address:

Website:

Budget:

WORKSHOPS

Workshop Name:

Instructor: Cost:

Date: Time:

Supplies Required:

Workshop Name:

Instructor: Cost:

Date: Time:

Supplies Required:

TRAVEL DETAILS

Flying to the Quilt Show

Airline Reservation Number:
_____

Travel Insurance:
_____

Departure Airport:
_____

Travel Date: _____ Departure Time: _____

Arrival Airport: _____ Arrival Time: _____

Flying Home from the Quilt Show

Airline Reservation Number:
_____

Departure Airport:
_____

Travel Date _____ Departure Time: _____

Arrival Airport: _____ Arrival Time: _____

Car Rental Information

Rental Company:
_____

Phone: _____ Pick Up Time: _____

Location:
_____

Reservation Number:
_____

Type of Vehicle:
_____

Drop Off Date: _____ Time: _____

Location:
_____

Driving to the Quilt Show

Travel Dates:

Miles to the Quilt Show: Miles from the Quilt Show:

LODGING INFORMATION

Hotel/Homestay Name:

Contact Name:

Phone:

Address:

Website:

Number of Nights: Cost:

Check in Date: Check Out:

QUILT SHOW CHECKLISTS

Pre-Show Checklist

- [ ] Pre-register online
- [ ] Preview Vendor List
- [ ] Sign up for Workshop(s)
- [ ] Preview Demo List

At the Quilt Show Checklist

- [ ] Set alarm reminders on your phone for workshop and demonstration start times
- [ ] Review the registration packet for vendor, demonstration and workshop locations.
- [ ] Make note of where the bathrooms are located.

QUILT SHOW PACKING LIST

- Comfortable shoes (You'll be doing a lot of walking)
- Your favorite quilt shirt
- Shopping Bag
- Water Bottle
- Pen and Paper for taking notes
- Light Sweater
- Personal fan
- Snacks

- _____
- _____
- _____
- _____

Little Purse Kit

- Band-Aids bandages
- Antiseptic Wipes
- Ibuprofen (or aspirin)
- Clothes-pins
- Neosporin
- Small sewing kit
- Touchless opener
- Hand sanitizer

- _____
- _____

Overnight Bag

- Change of clothes
- Pajamas
- Medications
- Bathroom supplies

- _____
- _____
- _____
- _____
- _____

QUILT SHOW BUDGET WORKSHEET

Travel

Total Miles /   Miles per Gallon =   Gallons

Gallons x $ per gallon = $ Total cost

Airfare: Car Rental:

Food

Number of days x $30 per day =   Food Budget

Lodging

Number of nights x $ per night =   Total

Classes

Workshop Fees: $

Fabric!

$ per quilt shop x   number of shops = $

Travel _____

Food _____

Hotel _____

Classes _____

Fabric _____

Extra _____

TOTAL _____

QUILT SHOPS NEARBY

Dates: _____ Budget: _____

Store Name: _____ Phone: _____

Address: _____

_____

Hours of Operation: _____

Website: _____

Dates: _____ Budget: _____

Store Name: _____ Phone: _____

Address: _____

_____

Hours of Operation: _____

Website: _____

Dates: _____ Budget: _____

Store Name: _____ Phone: _____

Address: _____

_____

Hours of Operation: _____

Website: _____

ENTERTAINMENT NEARBY

Places I want to Visit

Name: _____ Phone: _____

Address: _____

_____

Hours of Operation: _____

Entrance/Ticket Fee: _____

Reservation Number: _____

Name: _____ Phone: _____

Address: _____

_____

Hours of Operation: _____

Entrance/Ticket Fee: _____

Reservation Number: _____

Name: _____ Phone: _____

Address: _____

_____

Hours of Operation: _____

Entrance/Ticket Fee: _____

Reservation Number: _____

CHAPTER FOUR

Quilt Retreats

"LIFE BEGINS AT THE END OF
YOUR COMFORT ZONE."

- NEALE DONALD WALSCH

RETREAT INFORMATION

Host Name: _____ Dates: _____

Address: _____

_____

_____

Website: _____

Contact Phone: _____

Cost: _____

INFORMATION CHECKLIST

Questions to ask Quilt Retreat host:

1. Will the bed linens be provided?

2. Will there be cutting stations set up for use?

3. Will there be plenty of full-size irons and ironing boards available?

4. How much sewing space will be available? (One person to a table or sharing?)

5. What type of sewing chairs will we be using?

6. What meals and/or snacks will be provided?

7. What other amenities are available on the grounds of the retreat center/facility?

TRAVEL DETAILS

Flying to the Quilt Retreat

Airline Reservation Number:

Travel Insurance:

Departure Airport:

Travel Date: Departure Time:

Arrival Airport: Arrival Time:

Flying Home from the Quilt Retreat

Airline Reservation Number:

Departure Airport:

Travel Date: Departure Time:

Arrival Airport: Arrival Time:

Car Rental Information

Rental Company:

Phone: Pick Up Time:

Location:

Reservation Number:

Type of Vehicle:

Drop Off Date: Time:

Location:

Driving to the Quilt Retreat

Travel Dates:
_____

Miles to the Quilt Retreat: _____ Miles from the Quilt Retreat: _____

QUILT PROJECTS I'M TAKING

Project 1

Name:
_____

Supplies Required:

- _____ - _____
- _____ - _____
- _____ - _____
- _____ - _____
- _____ - _____

Project 2

Name:
_____

Supplies Required:

- _____ - _____
- _____ - _____
- _____ - _____
- _____ - _____
- _____ - _____

Project 3

Name: _____

Supplies Required:

- _____   - _____
- _____   - _____
- _____   - _____
- _____   - _____
- _____   - _____
- _____   - _____
- _____   - _____

Project 4

Name: _____

Supplies Required:

- _____   - _____
- _____   - _____
- _____   - _____
- _____   - _____
- _____   - _____
- _____   - _____
- _____   - _____

EXTRA PACKING ITEMS

Little Purse Kit

- Band-Aids bandages
- Antiseptic Wipes
- Ibuprofen (or aspirin)
- Clothes-pins
- Touchless opener
- Neosporin
- Small sewing kit
- Small notebook and pen
- Hand sanitizer

Overnight Bag

- Change of clothes
- Pajamas
- Medications
- Bathroom supplies

- _____
- _____
- _____
- _____
- _____

- _____
- _____
- _____
- _____
- _____

QUILT RETREAT GAMES

Just like at a baby or wedding shower, who doesn't love a good round of themed games? However, our version is all about quilting! Here is a list of some of my favorite games to play at a quilting retreat.

Quilter's Bingo

Quilter's Bingo has actually become a pretty popular quilting retreat game. In fact, you can find several versions of the Bingo cards online, including one from Missouri Star Quilt Company. Here are two of my favorite versions to play.

1. BINGO CARD LISTING FUN THINGS TO DO OVER THE COURSE OF THE QUILT RETREAT

These things can include anything from sewing in your pajamas to completing a quilt block without seam ripping to finishing an entire quilt project before you leave. The possibilities really are endless.

To play this version, hand each participant a card as they arrive. Then explain that they will have the entire retreat to accomplish as many as possible. After each task is complete, they can mark off that square. Then, when someone finishes and entire row or column, BINGO!

2. BINGO CARD OF VARIOUS QUILT BLOCKS TO MAKE

Just as the first Bingo version, each participant will be handed a card as they arrive. Then, throughout to course of the retreat, they can choose to make the blocks that are on the card. When they complete an entire row or column, BINGO!

Quilting Trivia

Trivial Pursuit is one of my husband and I's favorite games. I'm continuously floored at the amount of seemingly 'useless information' he has stored in that brain of his. Therefore, quilting trivia seemed like the perfect game to add to my list of favorite quilt retreat games!

Playing quilt trivia can be as simple as writing down a list of questions and calling them out. The first person to raise their hand and answer correctly wins a prize.

However, you could also jazz it up a little and write all the questions down on a piece of paper. Each player gets their own paper to see if they can answer each question silently. Once everyone has their answers written down, the truth is revealed. The person that gets the most answers correct wins!

What's in Your Sewing Kit?

I got the idea for this game from a baby shower I attended many moons ago. In their version the game was called, 'What's in the diaper bag'. My first thought was how easily I could turn this into a fun quilters game!

To play, simply create a list of a hand full of common, and not so common, quilting notions that might be in a quilter's sewing kit. When all the players are gathered together with their sewing kits, begin by calling out one item at a time. The quilter who has the most number of items in their sewing kit wins!

Quilter's Jeopardy

I grew up watching Wheel of Fortune and Jeopardy every week with my grandparents. I was so attached to those shows that I shed a tear when Alex Trebek lost his battle with cancer. So, to celebrate his life's legacy, I decided to come up with a quilter's version!

To play, begin by creating a list of trivia questions that fall into 5 or 6 categories. I might humbly suggest using the main categories in this book: Quilt Shows, Shop Hops, Quilt Tours, Quilt Retreats, Barn Quilt Tours, etc. Or, another example could be something like: Quilt blocks, Notions, Fabric lines, Stitches, Basting, etc.

Next, create 5 questions in each category. Write each question and answer on the back of a note card with their matching quantities written on the front: $200, $400, $600, $800, $1000. Just like contestants on the Jeopardy television show, as each person calls a $, read the answer. Then, your 'contestants' will have to come up with the appropriate question.

To work your way through the board, you can either choose to complete each question/answer card or set a timer for a limited playing time. Either way, it's now time to answer the Final Quilter's Jeopardy question. For this one I like to come up with something that is not so easy to answer, but not impossible. For instance, "Inventor of the first functioning and widely used Sewing Machine." Answer: "Who is Barthelemy Thimonnier?"

Each final contestant will make a final bet. After everyone has written their final question answers, each is revealed one by one. The quilter with the most amount remaining wins!

Name That Quilt Block

This fun game can be played in one of two ways. The first is for you to provide either pictures or samples of a bunch of different quilt blocks. Then, holding each one up at a time see if your quilters can guess the block names.

The second version, and my favorite, is to write down the names of several different blocks and place them in a bowl. Have your guests each pick one at random. Then, see if they can make the block. At the end, when everyone is done with their blocks, the group has to try and guess which block each person drew!

CHAPTER FIVE

Quilt Tours

"I HAVEN'T BEEN EVERYWHERE YET,
BUT IT'S ON MY LIST."

– SUSAN SONTAG

QUILT TOUR INFORMATION

Tour Name: _____ Dates: _____

Tour Company Name: _____

Website: _____

Contact Number: _____

Address: _____

_____

Total Tour Cost: _____

1st Payment Due: _____ Amount: $ _____

2nd Payment Due: _____ Amount: $ _____

3rd Payment Due: _____ Amount: $ _____

Instructor Name: _____

Workshop included: _____

TRAVEL DETAILS

Flying to Meet the Tour Group

Airline Reservation Number: _____

Travel Insurance: _____

Departure Airport: _____

Travel Date: _____ Departure Time: _____

Arrival Airport: _____ Arrival Time: _____

Flying Home from the Tour Group

Airline Reservation Number:

Departure Airport:

Travel Date: Departure Time:

Arrival Airport: Arrival Time:

TO DO CHECKLIST

- Purchase Travel Insurance
- Check passport is up to date
- Make copies of all travel documents. Leave at least one copy with a loved one.
- Check with travel agent for any items required for trip, including project supplies.

EXTRA ITEMS PACKING LIST

- Passport
- Cell Phone / Tablet
- Camera
- Good Walking Shoes
- Insurance documentation
- Phone / Tablet Chargers
- Pen and Notebook
- Day time Travel bag

Little Purse Kit

- Band-Aids bandages
- Antiseptic Wipes
- Ibuprofen (or aspirin)
- Clothes-pins
- Neosporin
- Small sewing kit
- Touchless opener
- Hand sanitizer

PLACES / THINGS I WANT TO SEE / DO

CHAPTER SIX

Quilt Cruises

"PEOPLE DON'T TAKE TRIPS.
TRIPS TAKE PEOPLE."

– JOHN STEINBECK

QUILT CRUISE INFORMATION

Tour Name: _____ Dates: _____

Cruise Company Name: _____

Website: _____

Contact Number: _____

Cruise Ship Name: _____

Port of Call: _____

Boarding Time: _____

Insurance Policy: _____

TRAVEL DETAILS

Flying to Meet the Cruise Ship

Airline Reservation Number: _____

Travel Insurance: _____

Departure Airport: _____

Travel Date: _____ Departure Time: _____

Arrival Airport: _____ Arrival Time: _____

Flying Home from the Cruise Ship

Airline Reservation Number: _____

Departure Airport: _____

Travel Date _____ Departure Time: _____

Arrival Airport: _____ Arrival Time: _____

LODGING INFORMATION

Hotel Night Before Cruise

Name: _____ Phone: _____

Address: _____

_____

Website: _____

Check in Date: _____ Check Out Date: _____

Reservation Number: _____

Hotel Night After Cruise

Name: _____ Phone: _____

Address: _____

_____

Website: _____

Number of Nights: _____ Cost: _____

Check in Date: _____ Check Out Date: _____

Reservation Number: _____

SHORE EXCURSION INFORMATION

Name:

Date: Time:

Location:

Things to Remember:

BUDGET

Cost of Cruise:

1st Payment Due: Amount: $

2nd Payment Due: Amount: $

3rd Payment Due: Amount: $

Insurance Cost:

Airline Cost:

Hotel Total Cost:

Extra Spending Budget:

Total Cost of Cruise Adventure:

TO DO CHECKLIST

- Purchase Travel Insurance
- Check passport is up to date
- Make copies of all travel documents. Leave at least one copy with a loved one.
- Check with travel agent for any items required for trip, including project supplies.

EXTRA ITEMS PACKING LIST

- Passport
- Cell Phone / Tablet
- Camera
- Good Walking Shoes
- Insurance documentation
- Phone / Tablet Chargers
- Pen and Notebook
- Day time Travel bag

OVERNIGHT BAG

Use this bag on last night of cruise before disembarking.

- Change of clothes
- Pajamas
- Medications
- Bathroom supplies

- _____
- _____
- _____
- _____
- _____
- _____

NOTE: As most of your quilting supplies will be provided, the following items are NOT allowed to be taken on board a cruise ship:

- Full-size Iron
- Sewing Machine

QUILT PROJECTS

Workshop Name: _____

Instructor Name: _____

Supplies Required:

- _____   - _____
- _____   - _____
- _____   - _____
- _____   - _____

Extra Project 1

Name: _____

Supplies Required:

- _____   - _____
- _____   - _____
- _____   - _____

Extra Project 2

Name: _____

Supplies Required:

- _____   - _____
- _____   - _____
- _____   - _____

CHAPTER SEVEN

Fun on the Road

"TAKE ONLY MEMORIES, LEAVE
ONLY FOOTPRINTS."

– CHIEF SEATTLE

ON THE ROAD AGAIN

Across

3. Visiting multiple quilt shops in one trip

5. Gathering of fellow quilters in one place to sew

8. Home of Liberty of London

10. International summer Shop Hop Quilters _____

11. Famed Fabric store in the UK: _____ of London

13. Quilting tour on the sea

15. Manufacturer of Kaffe Fassett and Tula Pink fabric

Down

1. Quilt Town USA

2. Home of the International Fall Quilt Festival in the United States

4. Location of Australia quilt convention

6. Location of National Quilt Museum

7. When the ladies hit the road

9. Japan quilt festival location

12. A group of Quilters that meet once a month

14. Organized quilting travel adventure: Quilt _____

BLOCKS AND MORE BLOCKS

Across

9. How to watch time slip by

10. Three by three in every color!

11. One color fading into another

12. Sweet and tart fruit from Latin America

15. German implant that'll brighten up any table.

16. Birds of a _____

Down

1. Traditional block named for brothers Jean Baptiste and Pierre _____

2. Duck! These birds are at it again!

3. Round and Round we go stitching in the woods.

4. What the Queen's husband wears on his head

5. Worn in your hair or around your neck

6. American quilt pattern mistakenly assume to have Irish origin

7. Single or Double, this is great for every Bride!

8. Where Barn Quilt tours began

13. These flowers put Dorothy to sleep

14. A popular gas station in

A CUT ABOVE

Across

2. Surface used to cut fabric

3. Group of fabrics measuring 5 x 5 inches

5. Fabric made using wax

6. How fabric is measured

9. 18 x 42 inches of fabric

11. Type of fabric most often used in quilting

12. Group of pre-cut fabric measuring 10 x 10 inches

15. How fabric comes

16. Used with a ruler to cut fabric

Down

1. Fabric used on the back of your quilt

4. Piece of fabric cut to approximately 18 x 21 inches

7. Cutting fabric on the diagonal

8. Pre-cut fabric measuring approximately 9 x 21 inches

10. Group of fabric pre-cut into 2.5 inch strips

13. What's left after cutting out your fabric

14. Base measurement of fabric

IN STITCHES

Across

3. Traditional way of stitching

4. Stitch used to completely cover a section or edge

8. Basic decorative stitch used to give a 'finished look'

9. Item used on a finger to aid in hand stitching

11. A traditional stitch that sews over the edge of fabric

12. Machinery used to make stitching faster

13. Applique process

14. Practice of embellishing fabric - often used in hand stitching

Down

1. Type of stitch for traditional piecing

2. Standard seam allowance

5. Material used to stabilize and/or strengthen fabric

6. Item used to create stitches

7. Item used to push thread through fabric

10. Applique process also

NOTIONS

Across

4. Place to keep your needles and pins

6. Slang for a seam ripper

9. Premade Item used to draw specific patterns on your quilt top

10. Item used to hold fabric together while stitching

11. Item or type of ruler used to trace onto fabric

13. Notion used to mark your quilt top that will disappear

15. Specialty item used to measure seam allowances

Down

1. How thread comes

2. A specific type of binding fabric

3. Type of pencil used to mark fabric that you can wipe off

5. Aerosol glue used to hold quilt sandwich layers together

7. Type of scissors to cut thread

8. Name for a small iron suitable for travel

12. Specialty item used in turned edge applique

14. Notion used to measure and cut fabric

QUILTERS GONNA QUILT

Across

4. Japanese Sewing Machine Company

6. Are between fabric edge and stitched seam

8. The act of making a traditional quilt block

10. Also called "stuffed technique"

11. Newer, more artistic form of quilting

12. Process of quilting and piecing at the same time

13. Machine stitching on paper: _____ paper piecing

14. Presser _____

Down

1. Maker of the Viking sewing machines

2. What's left over after cutting out your fabric pieces

3. Add this to your quilt to let people know who made it

5. Using paper templates to hand stitch blocks: _____ paper piecing

7. Quilt made from loved one's clothing

9. Sewing machine company created by Swiss inventor Fritz Gegauf

```
M A R I N E R S C O M P A S S N R
T Y G G J L E E H W N O G A W Z T
F X L B N C A R O L I N A L I L Y
L Q L G Q I C M C N D M E Q Z O E
O R Y Z Q R R J A G B E R I K A O
W A R Z I V Z G S L P W M R U K G
E P K T Y O K Z N E X O X Q N L X
R O L N F O H L G I R W R S Y E V
B U O Z W C E N I N D N X X L A N
A S S E K W A H I A V D S S J F L
S K M M Q R H N G Q R I E K T K M
K A C T O P G T L Y R T H W X L M
E B T E V G S W T I I G L R S P I
T E V S L B T J L Y B V V I D M Z
Z N D O Z Z T M L R H J T Z A U L
F I R P R A I R I E R O S E V N D
W Y H T A P S D R A K N U R D F S
```

FLOWERS AND CIRCLES

Wedding Ring

Wagon Wheel

Snail Trail

Prairie Rose

Orange Peel

Oak Leaf

Morning Glory

Mariner's Compass

Iris

Flower Basket

Drunkard's Path

Carolina Lily

```
A T A R C A T H E D R A L H W W N
K F M A A U R F X B V Y L T U A K
C C P L S I E U M B F B Z K B P C
O Y W N E S L B Z A M Y G S N S B
L P D I L E L F E H J U P U F R A
B C M N K U H L E S T L Z Z S A F
S V A J G H E W O N I A P I L E H
R H S P M L K R N T C D J B A B Z
A S K Q P C I R N I E Y F B G E
G A I A K N I Z U P W E I B X R
G D M A E C N W L L I M D N I W D
E N X P U E N T H E L K L Q V N M
B R X D P U V Q N T T D F E E K S
H U O A Z F O U R P A T C H F C U
I H T K S E S S I K D N A S G U H
C C C R O S S A N D C R O W N R R
H Q L L G Q A Y N L O G G I H W
```

FOUR DIVISIBLE BY NINE

Pinwheel	Windmill	Split Nine Patch
Rain Fence	Maple Leaf	Hugs and Kisses
Four Patch	Cross and Crown	Churn Dash
Cathedral	Beggar's Block	Bear's Paw

```
N Y K C I R T D R A C P E U O H T
W T O C W B E W S R E D I P S E T
Y F D U T C H M A N S P U Z Z L E
Y D T C E L T I C S Q U A R E G M
S N O T V J F E E I K G C D P K E
W S S L Y P D V I L F Z H L S D I
Y R T H M L O H L N P J I D Z N H
G R M O L D M A I D S P U Z Z L E
H G K O R G K L A T E D A H E R B
Z H K F O M B A S K E T W E A V E
Y A W H B C A B K C G D V X N F O
T S J N L I I T S S D X R Y D I E
M E L Z Z U P H S I R I I D S R P
U L L A B W O N S E U A D X V G G
J T U J Y C O T L I A O D S X E E
U R L V R E D D A L S B O C A J Q
I B S W Q K T S I W T C I T L E C
```

PUZZLE BLOCKS

Old Maid's Puzzle	Storm at Sea	Spider's Web
Snowball	Celtic Twist	Pineapple
Jacob's Ladder	Irish Puzzle	Dutchman's Puzzle
Celtic Square	Card Trick	Basket Weave

```
S  S  Z  V  S  P  Q  Z  P  W  T  O  X  R  A  R  E
E  T  S  L  K  R  P  E  M  Y  Y  V  K  H  A  X  I
P  K  R  I  O  J  A  L  R  Y  Q  Q  Z  T  T  Q  G
I  V  A  N  O  H  U  T  Z  H  B  Z  S  G  T  D  H
R  D  T  N  C  O  I  F  S  L  B  K  J  Y  P  T  T
T  Q  S  C  S  O  R  O  A  D  C  G  Z  T  V  S  P
S  E  M  Z  O  A  K  M  B  I  N  C  Y  R  X  F  O
D  L  U  L  Q  J  S  O  W  E  L  A  C  C  D  A  I
N  H  I  Y  S  P  C  S  D  X  A  I  N  H  D  Z  N
A  M  M  N  R  C  N  K  T  T  U  U  Z  O  P  L  T
S  B  E  B  E  U  R  K  H  A  M  V  T  Y  O  D  E
R  S  R  V  R  R  M  P  J  A  R  E  M  Y  F  M  D
A  D  P  B  S  T  A  R  A  N  D  C  R  O  S  S  S
T  N  E  C  I  O  H  C  S  E  I  N  N  A  R  S  T
S  C  A  R  P  E  N  T  E  R  S  T  A  R  M  U  A
R  A  T  S  D  E  T  N  I  O  P  X  I  S  J  T  R
A  G  D  F  R  I  E  N  D  S  H  I  P  S  T  A  R
```

WHEN THE STARS ALIGN

Ohio Beauty	Annie's Choice	Star and Cross
Stars and Stripes	Six-Pointed Star	Premium Star
Moon and Stars	Kansas Star	Friendship Star
Eight-Pointed Star	Carpenter Star	Brunswick Star

```
Q N Q L R B G D H R C X G H Y C W
S F S I A Q Y Y X B C D X Q C U C
H Z K X M U R W H K Y M C L G V O
E K T G L I N C Y M Q A V P Z X O
X P Q R D L I U G S R E T L I U Q
A C M Q J T I Q N S S Z C F R E D
G Z E S W W I C H A G T V G S A C
O X P E Y E Q X N S E L V A G E C
N H A W Y E X D R D P L V D F U U
S L H A G K W Z I Q O I M E R X E
N B E Z X I C S A P H C R Y M Z W
O M V E C W T A X F S N A P D P M
I M R H H H B I V C K E G T H I B
T B F A G W I L K Z R T N P G Z E
O H M I D L N A W Z O S O A T A V
N B R U O I Y I B F W Z L M Q R A
A D G E R P M F P H B H T D A D B
```

MISH MASH

Quilters Guild	Longarm	Midarm
Notions	Pinwheel	Quilt Week
Right Side	Sandwich	Selvage
Stencil	Hexagon	Workshop

CHAPTER EIGHT
Quilt Coloring Pages

"ALWAYS TAKE
THE SCENIC ROUTE."

BABY DIAMOND

Find the pattern for this quilt at
RonatheRibbiter.com/product/baby-diamond-quilt-pattern-printed/

AFRICAN VIOLET

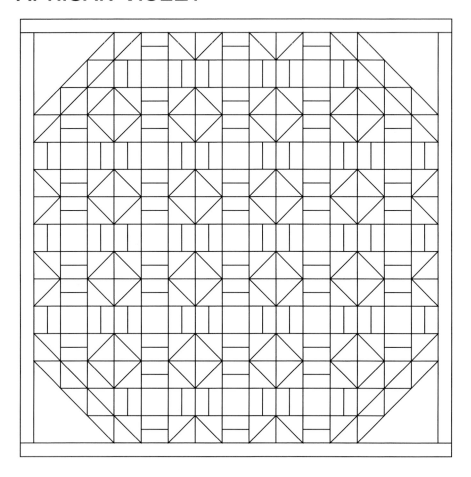

Find the pattern for this quilt at
RonatheRibbiter.com/product/african-violet-quilt-pattern-printed/

NOVEMBER RAIN

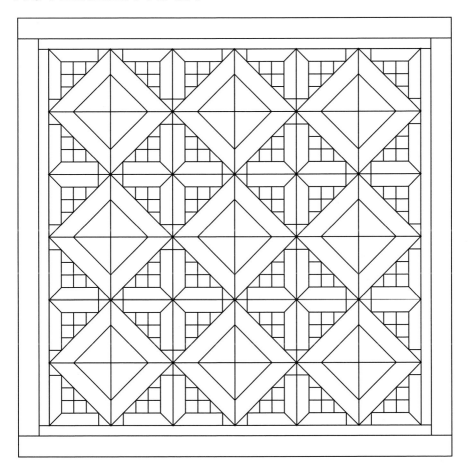

Find the pattern for this quilt at
RonatheRibbiter.com/product/november-rain-quilt-pattern-printed/

40 SHADES OF GREEN

Find the pattern for this quilt at the end of *Tips for the Traveling Quilter*

RAINBOWS ON OCEAN

Find the pattern for this quilt at the end *Tips for the Traveling Quilter*

STARGAZER

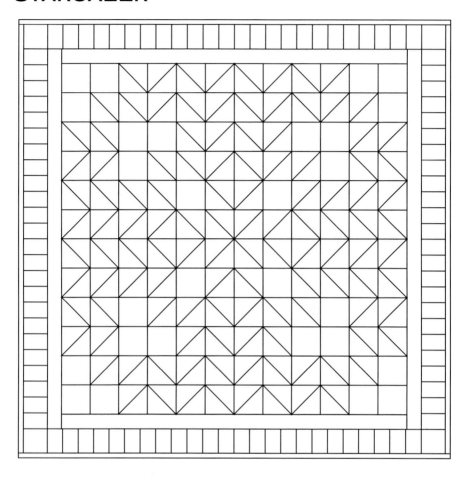

Find the pattern for this quilt at
RonatheRibbiter.com/product/stargazer-quilt-pattern-printed/

TWISTED

Find the pattern for this quilt at
RonatheRibbiter.com/product/twisted-quilt-pattern-printed/

ROSE WINDOW

Find the pattern for this quilt at
RonatheRibbiter.com/product/rose-window-quilt-pattern-printed/

WATER CRYSTALS

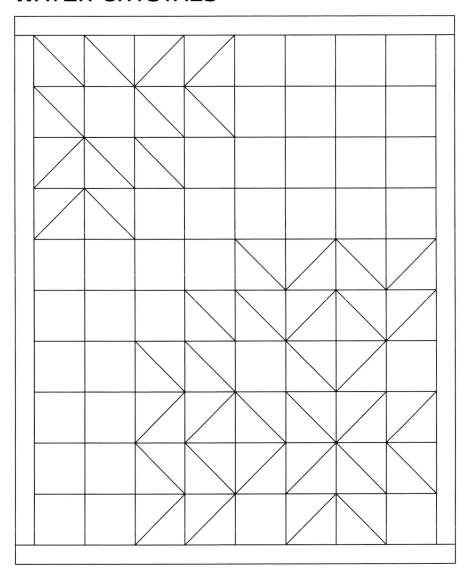

Find the pattern for this quilt at
RonatheRibbiter.com/product/water-crystals-quilt-pattern-printed/

CHAPTER NINE

Appendix

NOTES

DRAW YOUR QUILTY INSPIRATION

ANSWER KEYS

QUILTING CHEAT SHEET

NOTES

NOTES

NOTES

NOTES

DRAW YOUR QUILTING INSPIRATION

DRAW YOUR QUILTING INSPIRATION

DRAW YOUR QUILTING INSPIRATION

DRAW YOUR QUILTING INSPIRATION

Answer Keys

ON THE ROAD AGAIN

Across/Down answers:

1. HAMILTON
2. HOUSTON
3. SHOP HOP
4. MILBURN
5. RETREAT
6. PAH (PACAHATR...)
7. GRSTRP
8. UNITED KINGDOM
9. TOUR CACHOR
10. TREK
11. LIBERTY BNE
12. GUILD
13. QUILT
14. TOUU
15. FREE SPIRIT

BLOCKS AND MORE BLOCKS

1. LEMOYNESTAR
2. FLYINGGEESE
3. LOGCABIN
4. KINGSCROWN
5. BOWTIE
6. IRISHHAIN
7. WEDDINGRING
8. OISTTST
9. HOURGLASS
10. NINE PATCH
11. OMBRE
12. PINEAPPLES
13. PROPIS
14. CHEVRON
15. DRESDEN PLATE
16. FEATHER

A CUT ABOVE

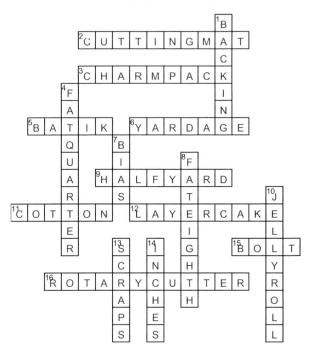

IN STITCHES

NOTIONS

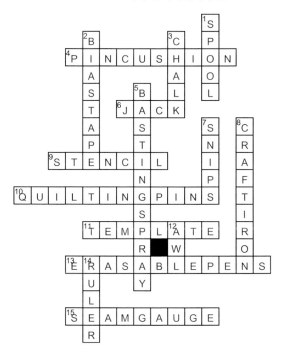

Across:
4. PINCUSHION
6. JACK
9. STENCIL
10. QUILTING PINS
11. TEMPLATE
13. ERASABLE PENS
15. SEAM GAUGE

Down:
1. SPOOL
2. BASTA PAP
3. CALL
5. BASTIN
7. SNIPS
8. CRAFT IRON
12. AW
14. RULER

QUILTERS GONNA QUILT

Across:
4. JANOME
6. SEAM ALLOWANCE
8. PIECING
10. TRAPUNTO
11. MODERN
12. QUILT AS YOU GO
13. FOUNDATION
14. FOOT

Down:
1. HUSQVARNA
2. SCRAPS
3. LABEL
5. ENGLISH
7. MEMORY QUILT
9. BERNINA

FLOWERS AND CIRCLES

```
M A R I N E R S C O M P A S S N R
T Y G G J L E E H W N O G A W Z T
F X L B N C A R O L I N A L I L Y
L Q L G Q I C M C N D M E Q Z O E
O R Y Z Q R R J A G B E R I K A O
W A R Z I V Z G S L P W M R U K G
E P K T Y O K Z N E X O X Q N L X
R O L N F O H L G I R W R S Y E V
B U O Z W C E N I N D N X X L A N
A S S E K W A H I A V D S S J F L
S K M M Q R H N G Q R I E K T K M
K A C T O P G T L Y R T H W X L M
E B T E V G S W T I I G L R S P I
T E V S L B T J L Y B V V I D M Z
Z N D O Z Z T M L R H J T Z A U L
F I R P R A I R I E R O S E V N D
W Y H T A P S D R A K N U R D F S
```

FOUR DIVISIBLE BY NINE

```
A T A R C A T H E D R A L H W W N
K F M A A U R F X B V Y L T U A K
C C P L S I E U M B F B Z K B P C
O Y W N E S L B Z A M Y G S N S B
L P D I L E L F E H J U P U F R A
B C M N K U H L E S T L Z Z S A F
S V A J G H E W O N I A P I L E H
R H S P M L K R N T C D J B A B Z
A S K Q P C I R N I N E Y F B G E
G A I A K N K I Z U P W E I B X R
G D M A E C N W L L I M D N I W D
E N X P U E N T H E L K L Q V N M
B R X D P U V Q N T T D F E E K S
H U O A Z F O U R P A T C H F C U
I H T K S E S S I K D N A S G U H
C C R O S S A N D C R O W N R R
H Q L L G Q A Y N L O G G G I H W
```

PUZZLE BLOCKS

```
N  Y  K  C  I  R  T  D  R  A  C  P  E  U  O  H  T
W  T  O  C  W  B  E  W  S  R  E  D  I  P  S  E  T
Y  F  D  U  T  C  H  M  A  N  S  P  U  Z  Z  L  E
Y  D  T  C  E  L  T  I  C  S  Q  U  A  R  E  G  M
S  N  O  T  V  J  F  E  I  K  G  C  D  P  K  E
W  S  S  L  Y  P  D  V  I  L  F  Z  H  L  S  D  I
Y  R  T  H  M  L  O  H  L  N  P  J  I  D  Z  N  H
G  R  M  O  L  D  M  A  I  D  S  P  U  Z  Z  L  E
H  G  K  O  R  G  K  L  A  T  E  D  A  H  E  R  B
Z  H  K  F  O  M  B  A  S  K  E  T  W  E  A  V  E
Y  A  W  H  B  C  A  B  K  C  G  D  V  X  N  F  O
T  S  J  N  L  I  I  T  S  S  D  X  R  Y  D  I  E
M  E  L  Z  Z  U  P  H  S  I  R  I  I  D  S  R  P
U  L  L  A  B  W  O  N  S  E  U  A  D  X  V  G  G
J  T  U  J  Y  C  O  T  L  I  A  O  D  S  X  E  E
U  R  L  V  R  E  D  D  A  L  S  B  O  C  A  J  Q
I  B  S  W  Q  K  T  S  I  W  T  C  I  T  L  E  C
```

WHEN THE STARS ALIGN

```
S  S  Z  V  S  P  Q  Z  P  W  T  O  X  R  A  R  E
E  T  S  L  K  R  P  E  M  Y  Y  V  K  H  A  X  I
P  K  R  I  O  J  A  L  R  Y  Q  Q  Z  T  T  Q  G
I  V  A  O  H  U  T  Z  H  B  Z  S  G  T  D  H
R  D  T  N  C  O  I  F  S  L  B  K  J  Y  P  T  T
T  Q  S  C  S  O  R  O  A  D  C  G  Z  T  V  S  P
S  E  M  Z  O  A  K  M  B  I  N  C  Y  R  X  F  O
D  L  U  L  Q  J  S  O  W  E  L  A  C  C  D  A  I
N  H  I  Y  S  P  C  S  D  X  A  I  N  H  D  Z  N
A  M  M  N  R  C  N  K  T  T  U  Z  O  P  L  T
S  B  E  B  E  U  R  K  H  A  M  V  T  Y  O  D  E
R  S  R  V  R  R  M  P  J  A  R  E  M  Y  F  M  D
A  D  P  B  S  T  A  R  A  N  D  C  R  O  S  S
T  N  E  C  I  O  H  C  S  E  I  N  N  A  R  S  T
S  C  A  R  P  E  N  T  E  R  S  T  A  R  M  U  A
R  A  T  S  D  E  T  N  I  O  P  X  I  S  J  T  R
A  G  D  F  R  I  E  N  D  S  H  I  P  S  T  A  R
```

MISH MASH

```
Q N Q L R B G D H R C X G H Y C W
S F S I A Q Y Y X B C D X Q C U C
H Z K X M U R W H K Y M C L G V O
E K T G L I N C Y M Q A V P Z X O
X P Q R D L I U G S R E T L I U Q
A C M Q J T I Q N S S Z C F R E D
G Z E S W W I C H A G T V G S A C
O X P E Y E Q X N S E L V A G E C
N H A W Y E X D R D P L V D F U U
S L H A G K W Z I Q O I M E R X E
N B E Z X I C S A P H C R Y M Z W
O M V E C W T A X F S N A P D P M
I M R H H H B I V C K E G T H I B
T B F A G W I L K Z R T N P G Z E
O H M I D L N A W Z O S O A T A V
N B R U O I Y I B F W Z L M Q R A
A D G E R P M F P H B H T D A D B
```

**GET MORE QUILTY TRAVEL ADVICE,
TRIP RECOMMENDATIONS AND
PROJECT IDEAS AT**

RonatheRibbiter.com